# Read, Write and Spell Book 1

## High Frequency Words
### by Joanne & Paul Duckworth

## Introduction

Read Write and Spell High Frequency Words Book 1 is one of a series of six books designed to reinforce the high and medium frequency words as identified by The National Literacy Strategy. Books 1 to 5 contain photocopiable worksheets designed as an aid for the busy primary classroom teacher, preparing word level work for the twenty minute independent session of the literacy hour. Activities include missing letters, missing words, word trails, true or false, mixed up sentences, sorting and matching, word searches and early spelling strategies. Children are also given the opportunity to collect each new word. The cartoon characters "Alf" and "Bet" are used to tell the pupils about each new activity. The words covered in this book can be found on the back cover and/or in the Pupil/Class record on page 3.

Topical Resources publishes a range of Educational Materials for use in Primary Schools and Pre-School Nurseries and Playgroups.

**For latest catalogue:**
**Tel: 01772 863158 or**
**Fax: 01772 866153**

Copyright © 1998 Joanne & Paul Duckworth
Illustrated by Pat Lamb.

Printed in Great Britain for "Topical Resources", Publishers of Educational Materials, P.O. Box 329, Broughton, Preston, PR3 5LT by T.Snape & Company Ltd, Boltons Court, Preston.
Cover design & Layout by Paul Sealey Illustration & Design, 3 Wentworth Drive, Thornton. 01253 865575

First Published September 1998
ISBN 1 872977 34 0

## Contents

The purpose of this book is to reinforce the high frequency words as listed in "The National Literacy Strategy". The photocopiable worksheets are designed as an aid for the busy primary classroom teacher, preparing word level work for the twenty minute independent session of the literacy hour. By using the activities in this book, the children will encounter each word at least three times - within the activity sheets and "Look, Say, Cover, Write, Check" word strips. It should be emphasised that the words need to be taught in a variety of ways, if the children are to retain them.

## Cursive Handwriting

Although the words on the worksheets are printed, the children should be encouraged to complete the worksheets in the cursive handwriting style of the school. This is of great importance, as research shows that the teaching of spelling should be linked to handwriting, as fully cursive script aids recall of letter order. Again, the "Look, Say ,Cover, Write, Check" word strips are printed. However, it would be useful for the class teacher to write each word cursively below, or in place of, the printed version before photocopying. The child will copy the cursive version rather than the printed one.

## Reinforcing the High Frequency Words

### Personal Targets
At the front of the book there is a "My Target Words Sheet." Each child could be given a number of the high frequency words as a personal goal to achieve in a set number of weeks. It is important to consider carefully whether the words given are achievable in the time allowed. The child with special needs may only be given five or six words whereas the child with a good visual memory could be given twenty or more. These personal target words could be added into weekly spelling lists or could be sent home as part of the homework programme.

### Achievement Certificate
Two Alf and Bet certificates have been included on page 5 to help reward the children's efforts in achieving their personal target.

### Word Games
Simple word games could be devised as a fun way to aid the learning of the words e.g. snap, pairs, word bingo etc.

### Mnemonics
A mnemonic is a device to aid memory, for instance to learn particular spelling patterns or spellings. These are a useful tool in helping the child remember the more difficult high frequency words. e.g.
**hear/here** - you hEAR with your ears
**Visual mnemonics** - like ju$^m$p

**Useful Word Cards** - Another means of reinforcing the high frequency words is to have them printed on cards. These can be kept either by individuals or in the "tidy baskets" on group tables so that the children have access to them at all times, whether writing a story or producing a piece of History, Geography or Science work.

**Use of Individual Word Banks** - Topical Resources supply an Individual Word Bank Book which pupils can use to either stick or write the high frequency words as directed at the end of many of the work sheets.

**Use of Personal Dictionaries** - It is useful for the children to make a bank of their own spelling errors. These can be added into their Personal Dictionaries.

**Classroom Word Bank** -After marking pupils' work the teacher will be aware of common class spelling mistakes. A few of these can be highlighted and displayed on a "Word Bank" noticeboard in the classroom.

## The Pupil / Class Record Sheet

This is designed to help the class teacher keep a record of children's achievements and to aid in the planning of future work. It would be useful at the beginning of the year to test the children to see which of the words they already are able to spell and this will dictate the work to follow. When a child has been tested three times on new words and spelt them correctly, the word could be recorded as learned. This sort of record is an invaluable resource for the setting of special needs Individual Education Plans.

## Look, Say, Cover, Write, Check Spelling Strategy

This book contains a number of fun ways of introducing the Look, Say, Cover, Write, Check Spelling Strategy. Teachers may enlarge, extend or change the words on these sheets to make these sheets appropriate to the needs of their class. Again, the class teacher should emphasise the importance of cursive script when practising a word.

## Extra Work for Early Finishers

Children who finish early could be encouraged to find the word they are working on within their reading book or other books of interest in the classroom. How many times does it occur? They could make collections of related words with phonic connections. e.g. old - sold, cold, holding, folded etc.

# Pupil / Class Record

We can assume a word has been learned when it has been either **tested** or **used correctly** at least three times.

Name: _____

Date Begun: _____

| | Tick or date | | |
|---|---|---|---|
| about | | | |
| an | | | |
| another | | | |
| as | | | |
| back | | | |
| ball | | | |
| be | | | |
| bed | | | |
| been | | | |
| boy | | | |
| but | | | |
| by | | | |
| came | | | |
| did | | | |
| dig | | | |
| do | | | |
| door | | | |
| down | | | |
| from | | | |
| girl | | | |
| got | | | |
| had | | | |
| has | | | |
| have | | | |
| her | | | |
| here | | | |
| him | | | |
| his | | | |
| house | | | |
| how | | | |

| | Tick or date | | |
|---|---|---|---|
| if | | | |
| jump | | | |
| just | | | |
| love | | | |
| made | | | |
| make | | | |
| man | | | |
| must | | | |
| not | | | |
| old | | | |
| one | | | |
| or | | | |
| our | | | |
| out | | | |
| over | | | |
| put | | | |
| ran | | | |
| saw | | | |
| seen | | | |
| take | | | |
| them | | | |
| then | | | |
| three | | | |
| tree | | | |
| us | | | |
| want | | | |
| way | | | |
| will | | | |
| with | | | |
| | | | |

Name:_____ Date _____

# My Target Words

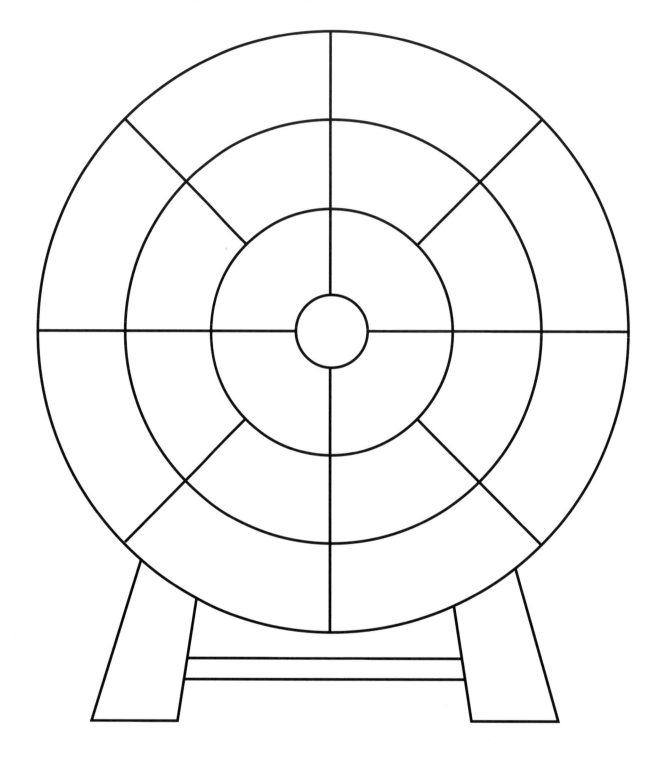

Over the next _____

I want to be able to read, write and spell these words.

Signed_____

# Well done

_____ !

You can read, write and spell
☐ words.

Signed **Bet** 😊 and _____ (Class Teacher)

Now set a target
for next time.

Date _____

---

# Well done

_____ !

You can read, write and spell
☐ words.

Signed **Alf** 😊 and _____ (Class Teacher)

Now set a target
for next time.

Date _____

Name: _____

boy

girl

I am a _ _ _ _ _

I am a _ _ _ _

Put **ir** words in my birthday cake.

Make **oy** words in my toy box.

Happy birthday

toy box

first
skirt
shirt
truck
crisp

t _ _ _
j _ _ _
b _ _ _

girl _____

boy _____

Colour **boy**, blue and **girl** green.

Colour the **ir** words yellow.
Colour the **oy** words blue.

| a | b | e | a | e | h |
|---|---|---|---|---|---|
| e | o | g | i | r | l |
| s | y | i | o | y | a |
| g | f | r | y | c | g |
| i | o | l | a | m | r |
| r | g | i | r | l | b |
| l | b | o | y | b | o |
| c | o | w | b | o | y |
| a | n | n | o | y | h |

| first | girl | royal |
|---|---|---|
| soil | fern | destroy |
| birthday | enjoy | boy |
| third | chirp | annoy | skirt |

Keep these words.

boy | girl

Name:_____

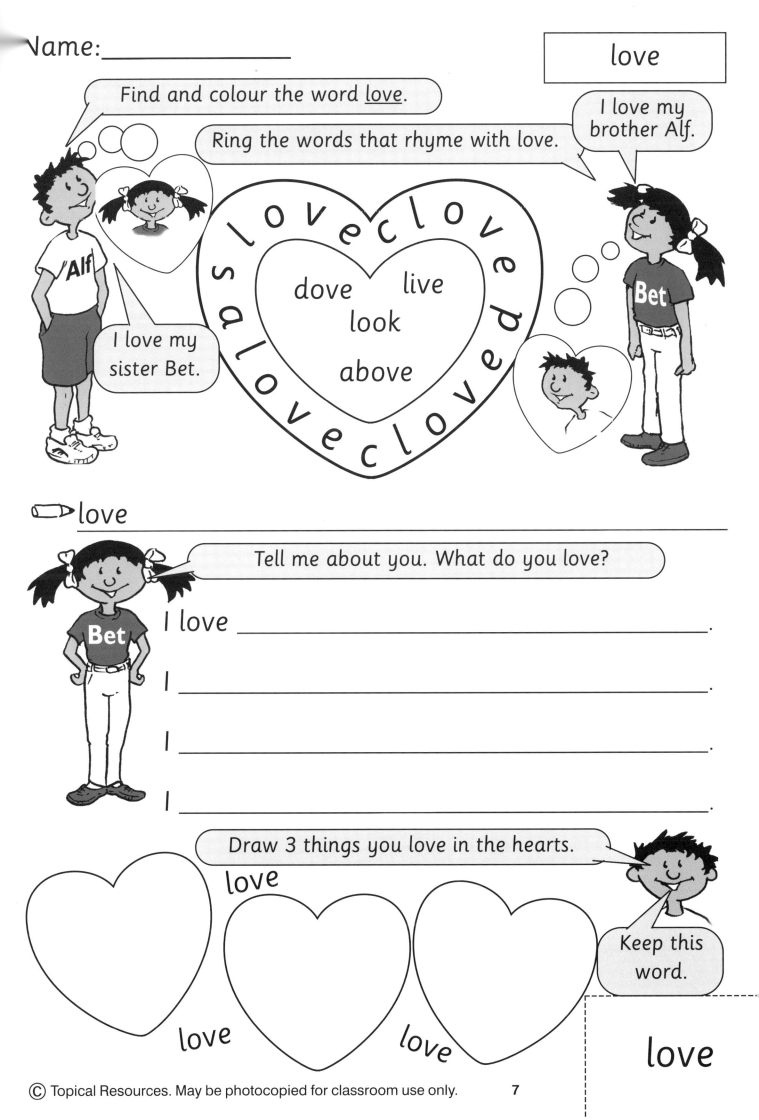

Find and colour the word <u>love</u>.

Ring the words that rhyme with love.

love

I love my brother Alf.

I love my sister Bet.

s l o v e c l o v e
s a l o v e c l o v e d

dove    live
look
above

love

Tell me about you. What do you love?

I love _____.

I _____.

I _____.

I _____.

Draw 3 things you love in the hearts.

love

love                    love

Keep this word.

love

7

Name:_____

our

house

This is our house.

Label our house

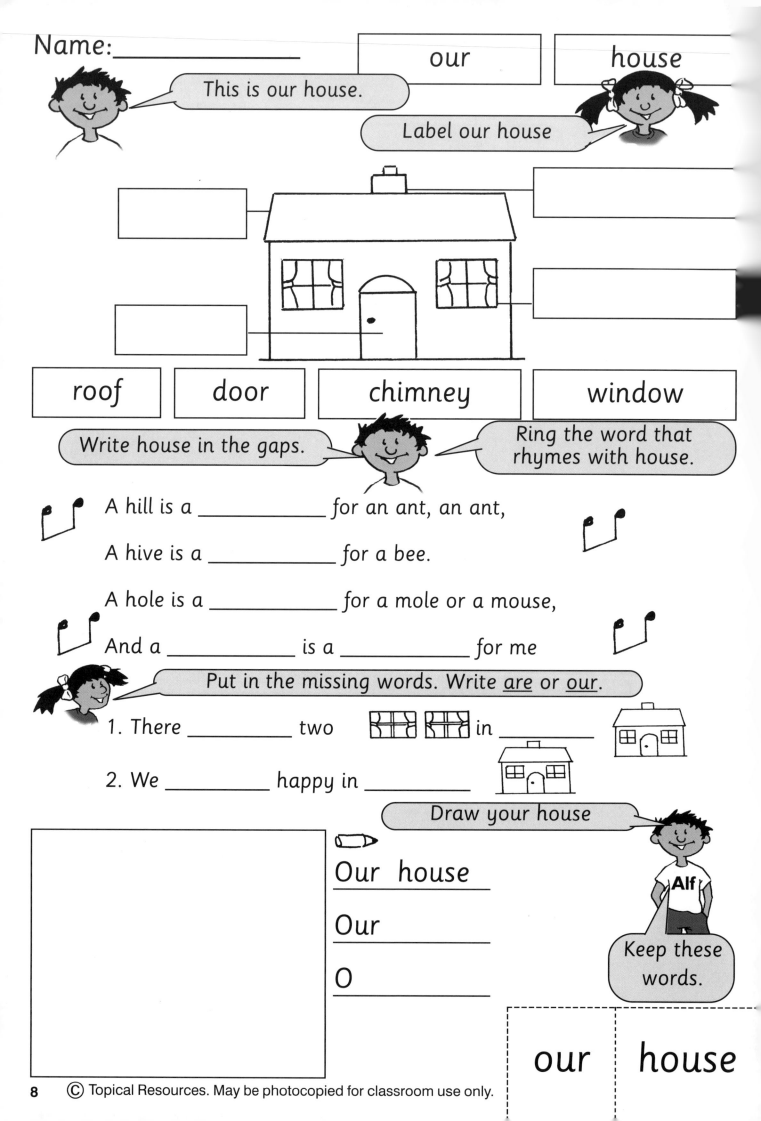

| roof | door | chimney | window |

Write house in the gaps.

Ring the word that rhymes with house.

A hill is a _____ for an ant, an ant,

A hive is a _____ for a bee.

A hole is a _____ for a mole or a mouse,

And a _____ is a _____ for me

Put in the missing words. Write _are_ or _our_.

1. There _____ two [] [] in _____

2. We _____ happy in _____

Draw your house

Our house

Our

O

Keep these words.

our   house

Name:_____

Cut along the lines and make two doors that open.

cut                        cut

Put the **or** words on the doors.

fold                fold

Bet

| | |
|---|---|
| for | horn |
| floor | short |
| fork | door |
| room | rock |

cut                        cut

Fold here and draw one thing behind each door.

Colour one door yellow and the other door green.

Which is your favourite door? - yellow or green?

Finish the sentences.

Behind the yellow _____ is a _____.

Behind the green _____ is a _____.

or _____

door _____

Keep these words.

or    door

    **9**

Name: _____

Shh! Bet is asleep in bed.

# bed

YAWN! Maybe I should go to bed too!

✏️ bed _____

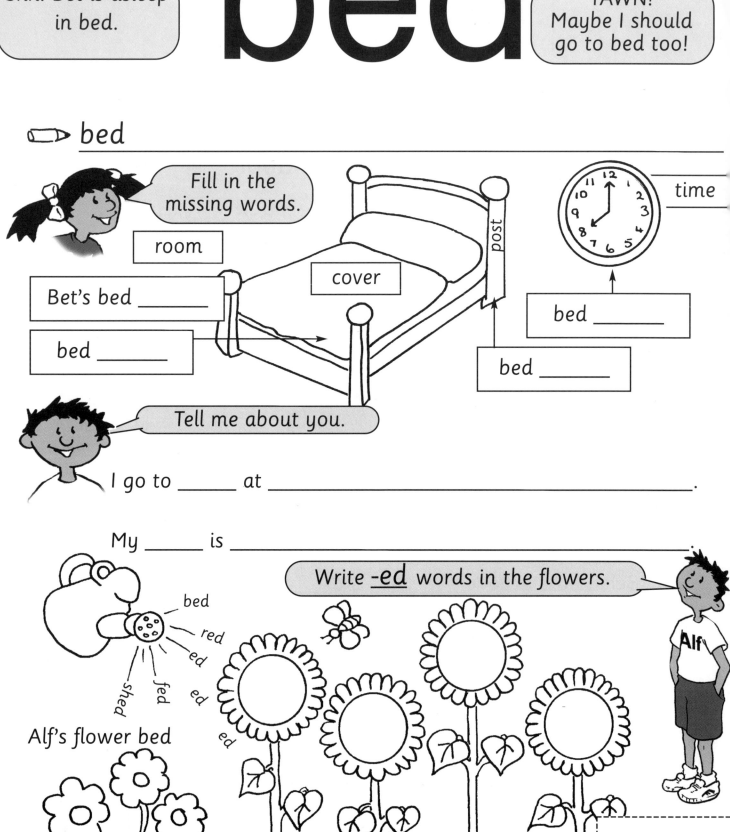

Fill in the missing words.

room

Bet's bed _____

bed _____

cover

post

time

bed _____

bed _____

Tell me about you.

I go to _____ at _____.

My _____ is _____.

bed
red
ed
fed
shed
ed
ed

Alf's flower bed

Write -ed words in the flowers.

bed

Name:_____

his | her

My brother has a snake. His snake goes hiss!

Find and colour **his** in his snake.

azthistlewrthisbcwhistlefgmisxthistoryal

hiss!

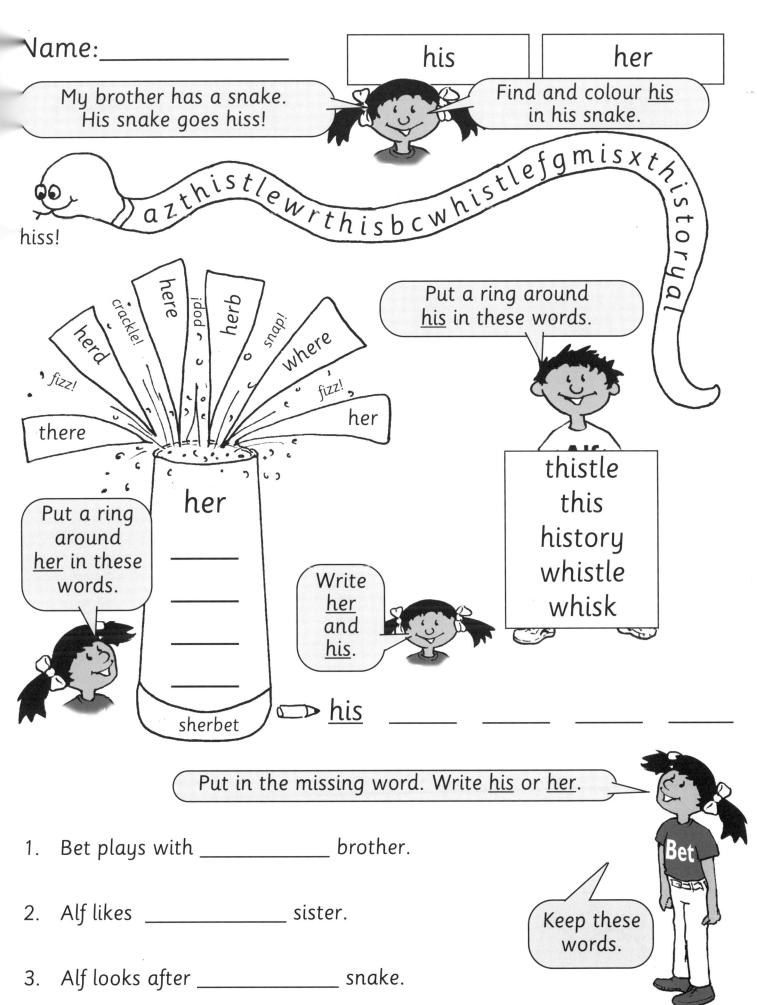

herd | here | pop! | herb | where | her
crackle! | fizz! | snap! | fizz!
there

Put a ring around **her** in these words.

**her**

_____
_____
_____
_____

sherbet

Write **her** and **his**.

Put a ring around **his** in these words.

thistle
this
history
whistle
whisk

**his** ___ ___ ___ ___

Put in the missing word. Write **his** or **her**.

1. Bet plays with _____ brother.

2. Alf likes _____ sister.

3. Alf looks after _____ snake.

4. Bet enjoys eating _____ sherbet.

Keep these words.

**his** | **her**

11

Name:_____

boy    girl    love    our    house

or    door    bed    his    her

Name:_____

three     tree

3

Write the words <u>tree</u> and <u>three</u>.

Write more <u>ee</u> words in the tree.

_ _ _ _ _

_ _ _ _

feet

heel

bee

✐ three _____

✐ tree _____

Fill in the missing words. Write <u>three</u> and <u>tree</u>.

1. There are 3 _____ wheels on a tricycle.

2. I want to climb a  _____.

3. Conkers grow on a chestnut _____.

4. A triangle △ has 3 _____ sides.

Draw three 🍎 on the tree.

Keep these words.

Bet

three   tree

Name:_____

Colour the word <u>out</u> in yellow.

We are going <u>out</u>.

and <u>about</u>.

Ring the word <u>about</u>.

outgeaboutsr

waotniabouts

Alf

Bet

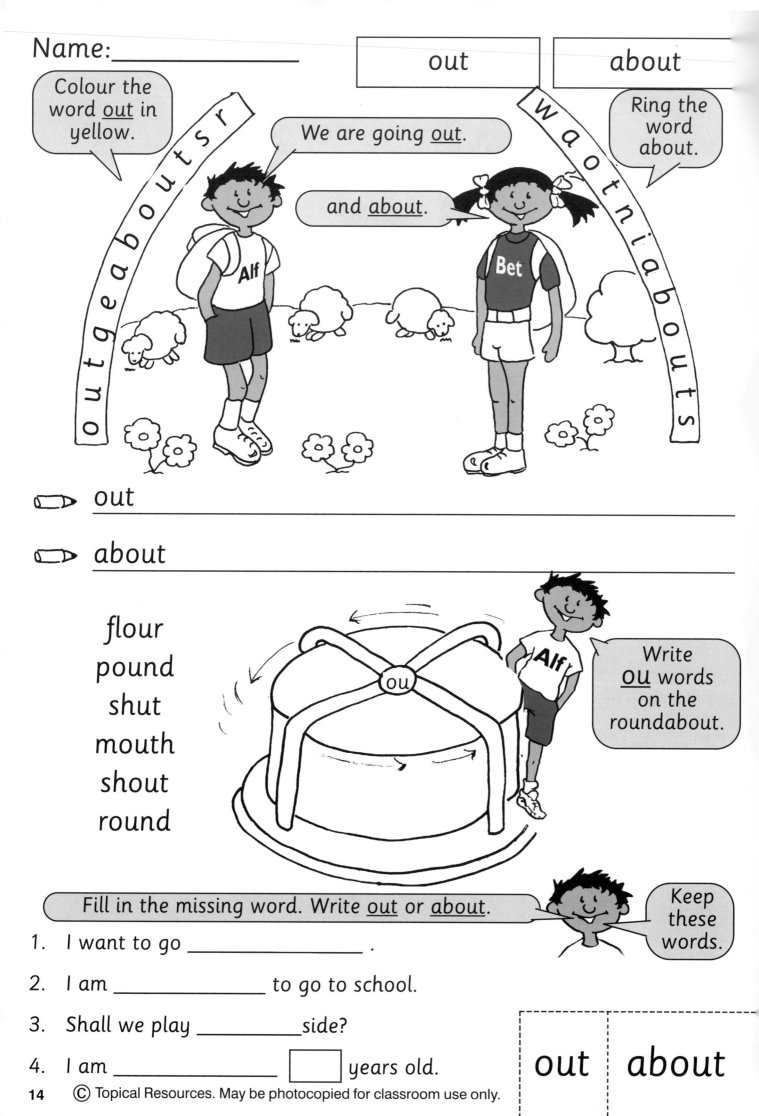

✏ out _____

✏ about _____

flour
pound
shut
mouth
shout
round

ou

Alf

Write <u>ou</u> words on the roundabout.

Fill in the missing word. Write <u>out</u> or <u>about</u>.

Keep these words.

1. I want to go _____ .

2. I am _____ to go to school.

3. Shall we play _____side?

4. I am _____ ☐ years old.

**14**  © Topical Resources. May be photocopied for classroom use only.

out | about

Name:_____

| put | but |

Write the full word.

Put in the missing word.

p u t ⟹ put _____ ⟹ I _____ on my coat.

c _ _ ⟹ cut _____ ⟹ I _____ my finger.

b _ _ ⟹ _____ ⟹ _____ I did not cry.

h _ _ ⟹ _____ ⟹ I went to the scout _____ .

n _ _ ⟹ _____ ⟹ I ate a pea _____ .

Put **ut** words in the hut.

Tick the words that rhyme with **put**.

| ✔ | but |
|---|---|
| | pit |
| | pat |
| | cut |
| | sit |
| | nut |
| | hit |
| | hut |
| | hot |
| | cot |

Keep ouT! Alf and Bet

Look at Sam Snake. Colour **put** red. Colour **but** yellow.

but _____

put _____

_____ these words away

_____ don't lose them!

Fill in the gaps.

Keep these words.

put | but

**15**

Name:_____

| ran | man |

My Dad drives a van.

Put **an** words in the van.

can  jam  fan

pan  ram  tan

Alf

Put in the missing word. Is it <u>ran</u> or <u>man</u>?

1. Alf _____ 50 metres on sports day.

2. Bet's dad is a _____.

3. The young _____ _____ down the street.

4. Bet _____ home from school.

Write the full word. Put in the missing word.

m <u>a</u> n  ⟹ <u>man</u>_____  ⟹  Dad is a _____ .

r __ __  ⟹ <u>ran</u>_____  ⟹  Alf _____ a race.

c __ __  ⟹ _____  ⟹  Bet _____ run fast.

v __ __  ⟹ _____  ⟹  Dad drives a _____ .

p __ __  ⟹ _____  ⟹  Put the _____ on the cooker.

t m a n f c a n t r a n k m a n f r a n t m a n c

Colour <u>man</u> red.
Colour <u>ran</u> blue.

Run, run, as fast as you can,
You can't catch me. I'm the gingerbread man!

Keep these words.

<u>man</u> _____ _____ _____

<u>ran</u> _____ _____ _____

| ran | man |

Name:_____

___ot

not    got

Put **ot** words in the pot.

Ring <u>not</u> in these words.

hot
cot
coat
dot
lot
hop

notice
another
note
nothing

got _____

not _____

What have you got? What have you not got?

I have got _____ .

I have not got _____ .

I have got _____ .

I have not got _____ .

Put in the missing word.

Write <u>not</u> or <u>got</u>.

1.  Bet _____ an apple from the tree.

2.  Alf did _____ win the race.

| n | o | t | g | o | t |
|---|---|---|---|---|---|
| o | o | n | o | t | n |
| t | g | o | t | g | o |
| g | o | t | n | o | t |
| o | t | g | o | t | g |
| t | g | o | t | t | o |

Colour <u>not</u> red.
Colour <u>got</u> blue.

Keep these words.

not    got

17

Name:_____

| three | tree | out | about | put |
|-------|------|-----|-------|-----|
|       |      |     |       |     |
|       |      |     |       |     |
|       |      |     |       |     |
|       |      |     |       |     |
| but   | ran  | man | not   | got |
|       |      |     |       |     |
|       |      |     |       |     |
|       |      |     |       |     |
|       |      |     |       |     |

Name:_____

With or without?

 W _____

a hat

W _____

a hat

W _____

a smile

W _____

a smile

Complete these sentences. Ring the word <u>with</u>

1.  I live with _____.

2.  I play with _____.

3.  I eat _____ with my chips.

with _____

Colour <u>out</u> yellow.
Colour <u>with</u> red.

Bet

Ring <u>out</u> in these words.

| a | h | o | u | t | c | i |
|---|---|---|---|---|---|---|
| j | g | u | w | i | t | h |
| w | i | t | h | w | w | e |
| i | o | u | t | i | i | w |
| t | u | o | u | t | t | i |
| t | h | u | b | h | h | t |
| d | f | t | w | i | t | h |

shouting

about

trout

spout

outer

outing

route

Keep this word.

with

19

Name:_____

do

dig

Bet is digging in her garden.

Join the dots. Which word?

Find the word dig in my spade and colour it.

What can you do in the garden?

Alf

Bet

dig
dim    dim
dig

did

dig

die

dig

I can _____

I can _____

do

Ring do in these words

done
adore
dove
ado
doodle
idol

Make a list of things to do today

Bet

| dim | dig |
|-----|-----|
| dip | |
| din | dim |
| did | |
| dip | dig |

1. _____

2. _____

3. _____

4. _____

🖍️ dig _____

🖍️ do _____

do or dig

Keep this word.

I _____ up potatoes.

I can _____ some gardening.

I need to _____ some weeding.

dig

Name:_____

| ball | will |

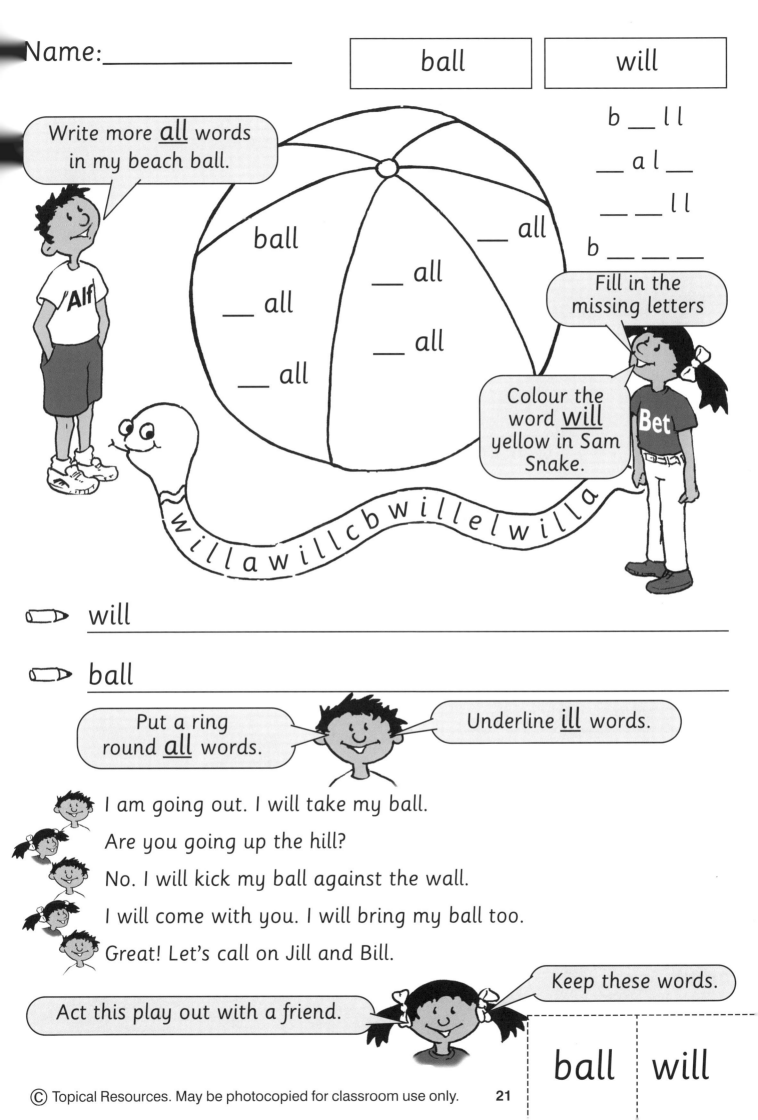

Write more **all** words in my beach ball.

ball

__ all

__ all

__ all

__ all

__ all

__ all

b __ ll

__ a l __

__ __ ll

b __ __ __

Fill in the missing letters

Colour the word **will** yellow in Sam Snake.

w i l l a w i l l c b w i l l e l w i l l a

Alf

Bet

✏ will _____

✏ ball _____

Put a ring round **all** words.

Underline **ill** words.

I am going out. I will take my ball.

Are you going up the hill?

No. I will kick my ball against the wall.

I will come with you. I will bring my ball too.

Great! Let's call on Jill and Bill.

Keep these words.

Act this play out with a friend.

ball | will

21

Name:_____

| just | jump |
|------|------|

Write the word here.

I am _____ in time.

I can do the long _____.

I _____ love playing games.

A horse can _____.

| | | | |
|---|---|---|---|
| | | | |
| | | | |
| | | | |

Colour just yellow.
Colour jump red.

Write j words in the jumper.

| f | f | j | u | s | t | s | t |
|---|---|---|---|---|---|---|---|
| t | j | u | t | j | u | m | p |
| j | u | s | t | j | u | m | p |
| u | s | t | j | u | s | t | j |
| s | t | j | u | m | p | j | u |
| t | j | u | m | p | k | u | s |
| j | u | m | p | j | u | s | t |
| o | m | p | f | f | t | t | f |

Bet

jug

Write just and jump here.

Tick the words that rhyme with jump.

Write the rhyming words here.

just _____

_____

jump _____

_____

lump [ ]

bump [ ]

jog [ ]

dump [ ] _____

junk [ ] _____

joke [ ] _____

lamb [ ] _____

pump [ ] _____

hump [ ] _____

Keep these words.

| just | jump |
|------|------|

Name:_____

Alf sent me a letter. Can you read it?
Underline the words:- with  love  from

Fill in the missing letters.

Dear

 would like you **2** come **2**

my birthday party on  day.

 hope you

with ♡ love from

w __ t __
lo __ __
f __ o __
__ __ th
__ __ ve

| a | f | e | n | l | h | i |
|---|---|---|---|---|---|---|
| t | r | f | r | o | m | o |
| l | o | v | e | v | o | w |
| f | m | b | g | e | r | i |
| w | i | t | h | m | f | t |
| p | j | c | w | i | t | h |
| l | o | v | e | k | d | l |

Find the words <u>love</u>, <u>with</u> and <u>from</u> in the wordsearch.
Colour <u>love</u> red.
Colour <u>with</u> yellow.
Colour <u>from</u> blue.

Match the sentences with a line.

Bet

Bet got a letter            his sister, Bet.

Alf went camping           from Alf.

Alf loves                  with Bet.

Keep this word.

 with
_____

 love
_____

 from
_____

from

**23**

Name:_____

| as | us |
|---|---|

✏️ as _____

✏️ us _____

**Fill in the missing word. Write <u>as</u> or <u>us</u>.**

Mum and Dad look after _____.

It was as cold _____ ice.

The van passed _____, _____we walked away.

Ice Cream

**Sort out the sentences and draw**

1. big as a horse. It is as

   _____

2. small as a mouse. It is as

   _____

3. loud as thunder. It was as

   _____

**Find <u>us</u> in these words.**

| push | dust | hush |
|------|------|------|
| bus | gust | rust |
| must | use | trust |
| fuss | just | crust |

**Put <u>as</u> in these words**

p __ __ t

f __ __ t

m __ __ t

l __ __ t

c __ __ t

v __ __ t

| a | s | a | s |
|---|---|---|---|
| s | u | s | u |
| u | s | a | s |
| s | a | s | u |
| u | s | a | s |

**Colour <u>as</u>.
Ring <u>us</u>.**

Alf

**Keep this word.**

us

Name:_____

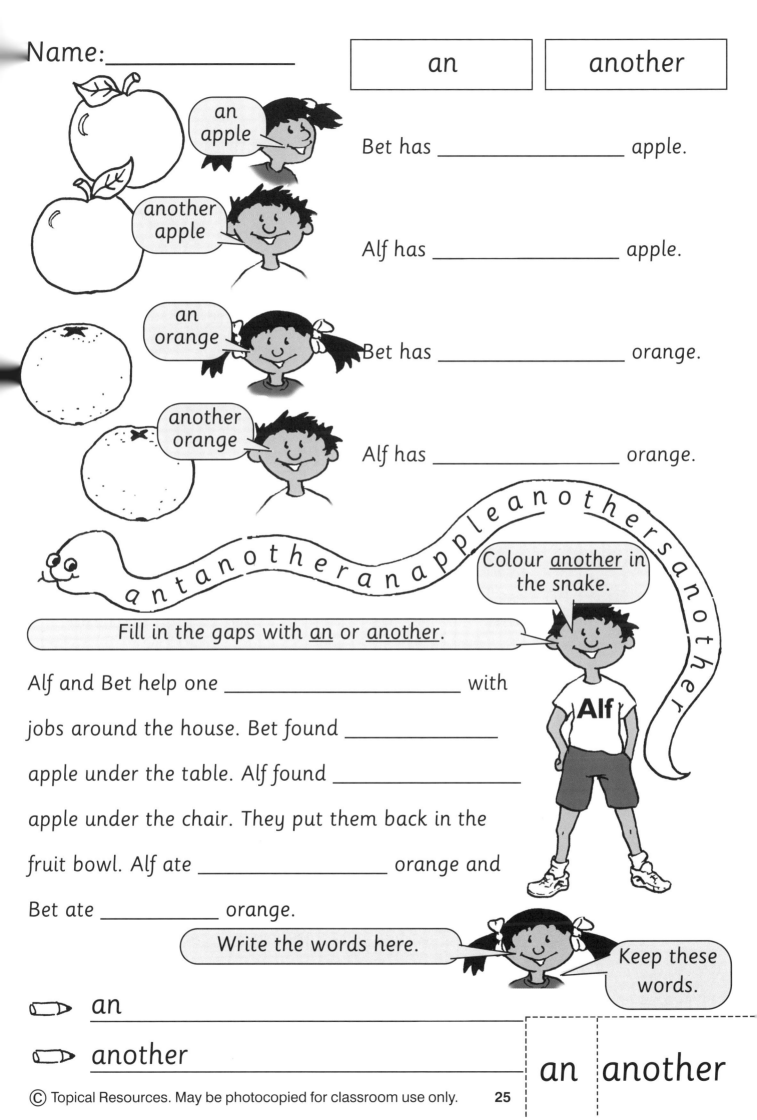

| an | another |

Bet has _____ apple.

Alf has _____ apple.

Bet has _____ orange.

Alf has _____ orange.

Colour another in the snake.

Fill in the gaps with an or another.

Alf and Bet help one _____ with jobs around the house. Bet found _____ apple under the table. Alf found _____ apple under the chair. They put them back in the fruit bowl. Alf ate _____ orange and Bet ate _____ orange.

Write the words here.

Keep these words.

an _____

another _____

an    another

Name:_____

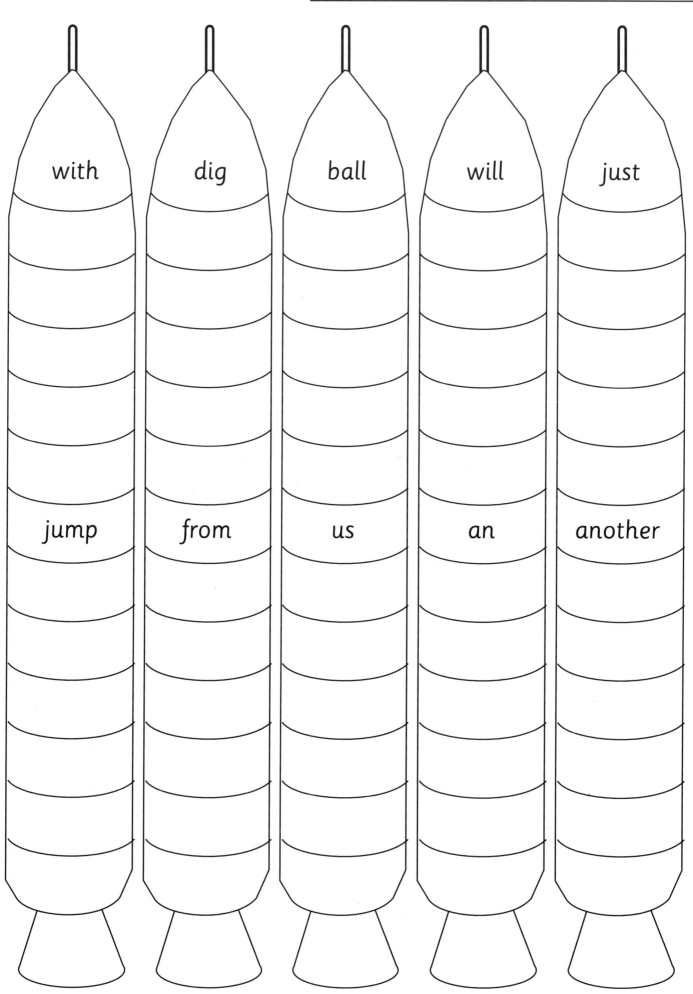

with

dig

ball

will

just

jump

from

us

an

another

Name:_____

| d | i | d |
|---|---|---|
| o | d | o |
| d | i | d |
| o | d | o |
| d | i | d |
| o | d | o |
| d | i | d |
| o | d | o |

Colour <u>do</u> in this grid.

Colour <u>did</u> in this grid.

| d | i | d |
|---|---|---|
| o | d | o |
| d | i | d |
| o | d | o |
| d | i | d |
| o | d | o |
| d | i | d |
| o | d | o |

do _____

did _____

Put in the missing word:- <u>did</u> or <u>do</u>.

Alf _____ his homework.

Bet can _____ the high jump.

Alf can _____ the long jump.

Bet _____ her reading.

Write down 3 things you can do.

1. I can _____

2. I _____

3. _____

What did you do just before you did this sheet?

Keep these words.

_____

_____

did          do

Name:_____

been | seen | tree | three

The ee bee only lands on ee flowers.

Colour the bee's ee stripes yellow.

Colour the flowers the bee will land on.

Write 2 more ee words in the empty flowers.

three

leg

soon

tree

seen

been

A play with Alf and Bet.

Where have you been?

I have been to our tree in the orchard.

Can any apples be seen on our tree?

Yes! I have seen three apples on our tree.

I wish I'd been there to see the apples.

Go and look! The tree is still there.

Put a ring round these words in the play.

Count the words.

been ☐   seen ☐   tree ☐   three ☐

been _____

seen _____

tree _____

three _____

Name:_____

Finish these sentences about my brother, Alf.

Choose <u>his</u>, <u>him</u> or <u>boy</u>.

1.  A lf is a _____.

2.  Bet is _____ sister.

3.  Bet likes _____ .

4.  Alf is a friendly _____.

5.  _____ pet snake is called Sam.

6.  Alf looks after _____.

Ring the correct word.

Write the missing word.

1.  This toy belongs to _____.

2.  This is _____ football.

him / his

him / his

Ring <u>him</u> in these words.

Fill in the missing letters.

thimble
chime
chimney
shimmer

b _ y

_ o _

b _ _

_ _ y

| b | o | y | h | i | s | b |
|---|---|---|---|---|---|---|
| o | a | h | i | c | b | o |
| y | h | i | m | b | o | y |
| h | i | s | b | o | y | h |
| i | m | b | o | y | h | i |
| m | d | o | e | h | i | m |
| b | o | y | h | i | s | f |

Keep this word.

Colour <u>boy</u>, <u>his</u> and <u>him</u> in the wordsearch.

him

**29**

Name:_____

girl | her | here

Finish these sentences about my sister, Bet.

Choose girl, her or here.

1. Bet is a _____.

2. Alf is _____ brother.

3. _____ is _____ ribbon.

4. This is _____ house.

Fill in the missing letters.

Change her to here!

her Add magic e ⟹ here

g __ r __

__ i __ l

g __ __ L

__ i __ __

Practice writing the word here!

✏️ here _____

✏️ h _____

Write the missing word.

Ring the correct word.

1. Bet's book belongs to _____.

her / here

her / here

2. My book is over _____.

| a | e | g | i | r | l | h |
|---|---|---|---|---|---|---|
| f | h | i | d | g | g | e |
| h | e | r | b | h | i | r |
| e | r | l | h | e | r | h |
| r | c | g | i | r | l | i |
| h | e | r | g | i | r | l |
| g | i | r | l | h | e | r |

Colour girl red, and her yellow in the wordsearch.

Keep this word.

Bet

here

Name:_____

✏️ as _____

✏️ has _____

a snake

a ball

a toybox

a flowerbed

a letter

Dear Bet,
Please come
to my party
on Sunday.
With love
from
Alf
x x x

a cake

a sherbet

a bed

**What do I have?**

Bet has _____

Bet _____

Bet _____

Bet _____

**What do I have?**

Alf has _____

Alf _____

Alf _____

Alf _____

**Fill in the missing word.**        **Write as or has.**

Alf _____ a flower.

As round _____ a ball.

Bet _____ some sherbet.

As flat _____ a pancake.

**Ring as in these words.**

pass    mask    ass    past

ask    mass    grasp    plastic

**Keep these words.**

as    has

Name:_____

Write the word **but** in the gaps.
Join the word to the correct picture.

__ __ __ cher    __ __ __ ton

__ __ __ ter    __ __ __ ler

| Butler | Button | Butcher | Butter |
|--------|--------|---------|--------|

**Find and colour the word but on the coat.**

**Ring if in the words.**

bit

bat

but

bet

**Write words which rhyme with but around the buttons.**

Bet

lift
sift
rift
drift
stiff
cliff

**Fill in the missing word. Excuses! Excuses!**

I want to fly b_____ I have no wings.

I want to dig b_____ ___ h_____ n___ spade .

**Match the sentences - if or but?**

Bet wants to write                    we wear cool clothes.

If the weather is hot                 if it is raining.

Alf uses an umbrella                  but she has no pen.

**Keep this word.**

✏ if _____

✏ but _____

if

© Topical Resources. May be photocopied for classroom use only.

Name:_____

| our | or |
|---|---|

_ _ _ house          _ _ _ cat          _ _ _ dog

**Answer the questions. Ring the word or.**

1.  Do you have a cat or a dog? _____

2.  Do you live in a house or a flat? _____

3.  Do you like chocolate or ice-cream best? _____

**Ring or in these words.**

| before |
|---|
| more |
| orange |
| horrible |
| door |
| poor |
| snore |

**Ring our in these words.**

| hour |
|---|
| pour |
| sour |
| yourself |
| flour |
| four |
| journey |
| colour |

or _____

_____

our _____

_____

**Can you fill the gaps? Write or or our.**

hot _____ cold.

_____ house.

_____ school.

wet _____ dry.

good _____ bad.

light _____ dark

_____ street.

**Try some of your own.**

_____ or _____ .

_____ or _____ .

our _____ .

our _____ .

our _____ .

Name:_____

| have | got |

candy floss

wow!

Bet

rock

toffee apple

Alf

roll up! roll up!

hotdog

goldfish

Finish the sentence.
Write <u>have</u> or <u>got</u>.

Tick ✔ true or false?

True    False

1.   Bet has _____ a hot dog. . . . . . . . . . .

2.   Alf and Bet _____ won a goldfish. . . . . . . . . .

3.   They _____ _____ a stick of rock. . . . . . .

Draw things you
have got in the
slot machine,

What have you
won at the fair?

win!  win!  win!  win!    10p

My
Story
Book

book

Alf: Ihave won a _____

Alf:I have _____

_____

Bet:_____

_____

Bet:_____

_____

Can you make
your own slot machine
to keep <u>-ot</u> words in?

Name:_____

old        by

I am six years old. How old are you?

I am _____.

How old is Bet?
Count the candles.

Bet is _____

years_____.

How old is your friend?

My friend is

_____.

Put in by or old.

| o | l | d | o |
|---|---|---|---|
| l | b | y | l |
| d | y | b | d |
| y | o | l | d |
| o | l | d | b |
| b | y | y | y |
| o | l | d | b |
| l | d | b | y |
| d | o | l | d |
| o | l | d | y |

1.  I have read a book [ ][ ] Eric Clarke.

2.  The [ ][ ] clock still goes tick-tock.

3.  The [ ][ ] car would not start.

4.  I cheered as the band walked [ ][ ].

Colour old red. Colour by Green.

old _____

by _____

Keep these words.

old   by

Name:_____

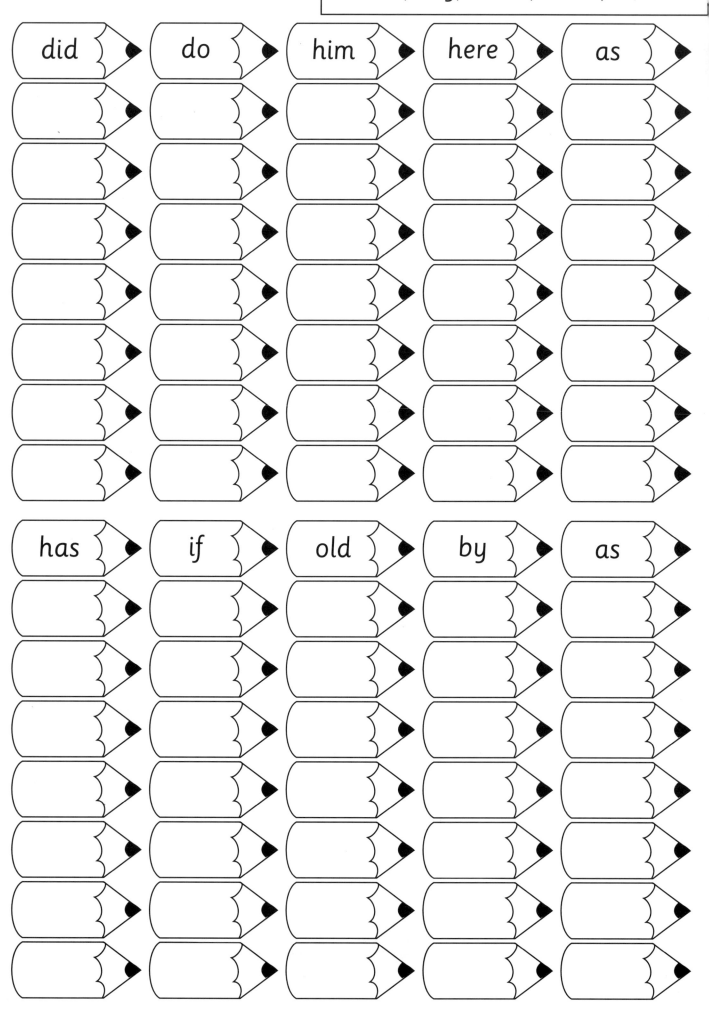

did   do   him   here   as

has   if   old   by   as

Name:_____

How now brown cow!

Put ow words in this cow.

Colour this cow brown.

how  down  won  now  owl  saw

Colour the word down brown.

a d o w n b f d o w n c d o w n e

I am going downstairs. Fill in the missing letters.

I've hurt my finger. OW!

_ own

d _ w _

_ _ wn

d _ _ n

d _ _ _ _

Put a ring round how in these words.

show    howl    shower

Answer the questions.

1. How old are you? _____

2. How do you come to school? _____

✏ how _____

✏ down _____

Keep these words.

how | down

37

Name:_____

Complete the cross word. Write <u>came</u> or <u>from</u>.

| came | from |
|------|------|

<u>Across</u>

4. Bet got a letter _____ Alf.

5. Alf _____ downstairs.

<u>Down</u>

1. Alf _____ into the house.

2. Bet walked home _____ school.

3. Bet got a present _____ her grandma.

✏️ came _____

✏️ from _____

Fill in the missing words.

Read the sentences.

Where did my Milk come from?

It _____ _____ a cow.

Where did my Wool come from?

Keep this word.

It _____ _____ a sheep.

came

Name:_____

| seen | saw | have |

Fill in the missing words.
Write seen or saw.

Read the sentences.

1. We have _____ some fireworks. ....... | s |  |  |  |

2. I _____ a butterfly. ................. | s |  |  |

3. We _____ an aeroplane. ............... | s |  |  |

4. He has _____ the teacher. ........... | s |  |  |

Colour saw yellow. Colour seen red.

s e e n s a w s e e n
s a w s e e n s a w

What have you seen on the way to school?

I saw _____

_____

I saw _____

_____

seen _____

saw _____

have _____

Keep these words.

saw | seen

Name:_____

Put **ake** in all the gaps.

Happy Birthday, Bet

Pat a c_____, Pat a c _____,

B _____ r's man.

M_____ me a c_____,

as fast as you can.

Say the rhyme.

make
_____

_____

Fill in the missing word. Write **made** or **make**.

1. I _____ my bed this morning.

2. He wants to _____ a cake.

3. She _____ a mess yesterday!

made
_____

_____

What have you made?

Keep these words.

I
_____

_____

make ┊ made

Name:_____

| him | her |

**Write him or her.**

Alf is Bet's brother. Bet is standing next to _____. He is standing next to _____.

Alf likes _____.

Bet likes _____.

Alf plays with _____.

Bet plays with _____.

✏ him _____

✏ her _____

**Put him in these words.**

**Colour him red. Colour her yellow.**

c _ _ _ e ⟹ _____

s _ _ _ mer ⟹ _____

t _ _ _ ble ⟹ _____

c _ _ _ ney ⟹ _____

_ _ _ self ⟹ _____

him his her have his his here her hum him his his here her his him here her his him him her his him

It's goodnight from _____ and it's goodnight from _____.

41

Name:_____

must      just

I'm late for school. I must hurry!

I'm just in time!

Alf

Bet

Write the fulll word.

Fill in the missing words.

j u_ s_ t_  ⇒  just  ⇒  I'm _____ in time!

m _ _ _  ⇒  must  ⇒  I _____ hurry!

d _ _ _  ⇒  _____  ⇒  Let's sweep up the _____.

g _ _ _  ⇒  _____  ⇒  A _____ of wind.

tr _ _ _ _  ⇒  _____  ⇒  I _____ you.

r _ _ _  ⇒  _____  ⇒  This metal will _____.

Colour must yellow and just red.

must rust just must trust gust just dust must

✏ must _____

✏ just _____

Finish the sentence.

Keep this word.

I must _____

_____ today.

must

Name:_____

| has | had | have |
|-----|-----|------|

Fill in the missing words.
Write <u>has</u>, <u>had</u> or <u>have</u>.

Read the sentences.

1. We _____ been to the park today. . . . . . .

| h | a | | |
|---|---|---|---|

2. We _____ a good time! . . . . . . . . . . . . .

| h | a | |
|---|---|---|

3. Alf _____ a snake called Sam. . . . . . . . . . .

| h | a | |
|---|---|---|

4. I _____ to go to school. . . . . . . . . . . . .

| h | a | | |
|---|---|---|---|

5. Bet _____ long hair. . . . . . . . . . . . . .

| h | a | |
|---|---|---|

6. She _____ a lovely birthday. . . . . . . . . . .

| h | a | |
|---|---|---|

Colour <u>has</u> blue, <u>had</u> yellow and <u>have</u> red.

has
has          had
    had
have         have
    had

Write the words here.

✏️ has _____

✏️ had _____

✏️ have _____

What have you done today?     Keep these words.

I
_____

_____ today.

| had | have |
|-----|------|

43

Name:_____

| how | down | came | saw | seen |
|-----|------|------|-----|------|

| make | made | must | had | have |
|------|------|------|-----|------|

Name:_____

| them | then |
|------|------|

✏ them _____

✏ _____

Fill in the missing word. Is it <u>them</u> or <u>then</u>?

I went upstairs, _____ I brushed my teeth.

I saw Mum and Dad. I asked _____ if I could play out..

First it thundered, _____ it rained.

Colour <u>them</u> green and <u>then</u> blue.

them the then there them

then that the then them

that then them then then

Bet

them them them      then then then

Tick the words that rhyme with <u>then</u>.

Can you think of any more.

| hen | ✔ |
|------|------|
| there | |
| men | |
| den | |
| them | |
| the | |
| pen | |
| ten | |

Write the rhyming words here.

_____

_____

_____

_____

Alf

then

✏ then _____

✏ _____

Keep these words.

| them | then |
|------|------|

45

Name:_____

| want | take |
|------|------|

**Ring take in these words.**

taken

mistake

taker

stake

**Write take in the gaps. Do you know the answers?**

6 _take_ away 2 = ☐

8 _____ away 3 = ☐

5 _____ away 1 = ☐

**What do you want?**

I want _____

I want _____

I want _____

**Colour want red and take yellow.**

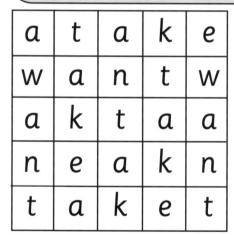

| a | t | a | k | e |
|---|---|---|---|---|
| w | a | n | t | w |
| a | k | t | a | a |
| n | e | a | k | n |
| t | a | k | e | t |

**Fill in the missing letters.**

w __ n __

__ a n __

w a __ __

__ __ n __

__ __ __ __ t

**Put in the missing word. Write want or take.**

1. I _____ my dog for a walk.

2. I _____ to go outside.

3. I _____ my money to the shop.

**Keep these words.**

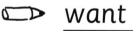 want _____

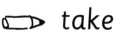 take _____

| want | take |
|------|------|

Name:_____

one    way

This is a <u>one way</u> sign!

Colour the sign blue. Leave the arrow white.

Write the word <u>way</u> in the gaps.

Which _____ do I go?  This _____

I have lost my _____ .

one

one

way

way

one   way

X

one

one

way

Colour the word <u>one</u>. How many?

Colour the word <u>way</u>. How many?

in

one

out

There is only one way round the maze!

Keep these words.

one _____

way _____

one  way

Name:_____

Fill in the missing words.

"Come _____ Bet," said Alf.

"You've gone the wrong

_____!"

this way    that way

Come back Bet. You've gone the wrong way!

that way

Sorry Alf.

"Sorry Alf," said Bet.

She _____ _____ to Alf.

Find and colour the word <u>came</u>.

| cane | come | came |
| came | camel | same |

Find and colour the word <u>back</u>.

back   duck   lack
buck   bake   back

Find and colour the word <u>way</u>.

| why | war | way |
| day | way | say |

Choose a rhyming word.

way  . . . . . _____

came  . . . . _____

back  . . . . _____

Fill in the missing words. Choose <u>back</u>, <u>came</u> or <u>way</u>.

1.  Alf _____ _____ to his house.

2.  He knew the right _____.

3.  Bet _____ _____ with him.

Sort out the sentence.

Keep this word.

came right  He back the way.

_____

back

Name:_____

| be | been |

Put in the missing word. Is it <u>be</u> or <u>been</u>.

Alf:- When I grow up I want to _____ an artist.

Bet:- When I grow up I want to _____ an actor.

Alf:- I have _____ to France on holiday.

Bet:- I have _____ to the swings

What do you want to be when you grow up?

I want _____.

Name 3 places that you have been to.

Write the <u>ee</u> words on here.

keep
feed
Ben
bed
been
seed

1. I have been to _____

2. I _____

3. _____

Next year Alf will be 7 years old. He has
been going to school for 2 years. He wants
to be an artist when he grows up. He has
been painting since he was three. He will be able to
do a lot more when he has been to High School.

green

Ring <u>be</u>.
How many?

Ring <u>been</u>.
How many?

be _____

been _____

Keep these words.

be | been

**49**

Name: _____

jump | over | down

**Alf and Bet's Sports Day**

Fill in the missing words. Write jump, over or down.

| | | | |
|---|---|---|---|
| Bet can _____ _____ the pole. | Alf runs _____ the lane. | Bet _____ takes the others. | Alf can _____ a long way |

Can you do this crossword puzzle? Look at the clues across. Look at the clues down.

<u>Across</u>

1. Bet runs d_____ the lane.

3. Alf can do the high j_____.

5. Bet jumps o_____ the pole.

6. Alf and Bet fall d_____ in the three-legged race.

7. Bet can j_____ a long way.

<u>Down</u>

2. Alf o_____ takes Bet.

3. Bet can j_____ in the sack race.

4. Alf's egg falls d_____ on the ground.

5. Bet wins! She is o_____ the moon!

Crossword grid:
```
          1 d  2
 3 j
                    4
    5 o
                6
                    n
        7 j
```

Sort out the sentences.

a long Alf way. jump can

✏ _____

the Bet down lane. runs

✏ _____

Keep this word.

over

Name:_____

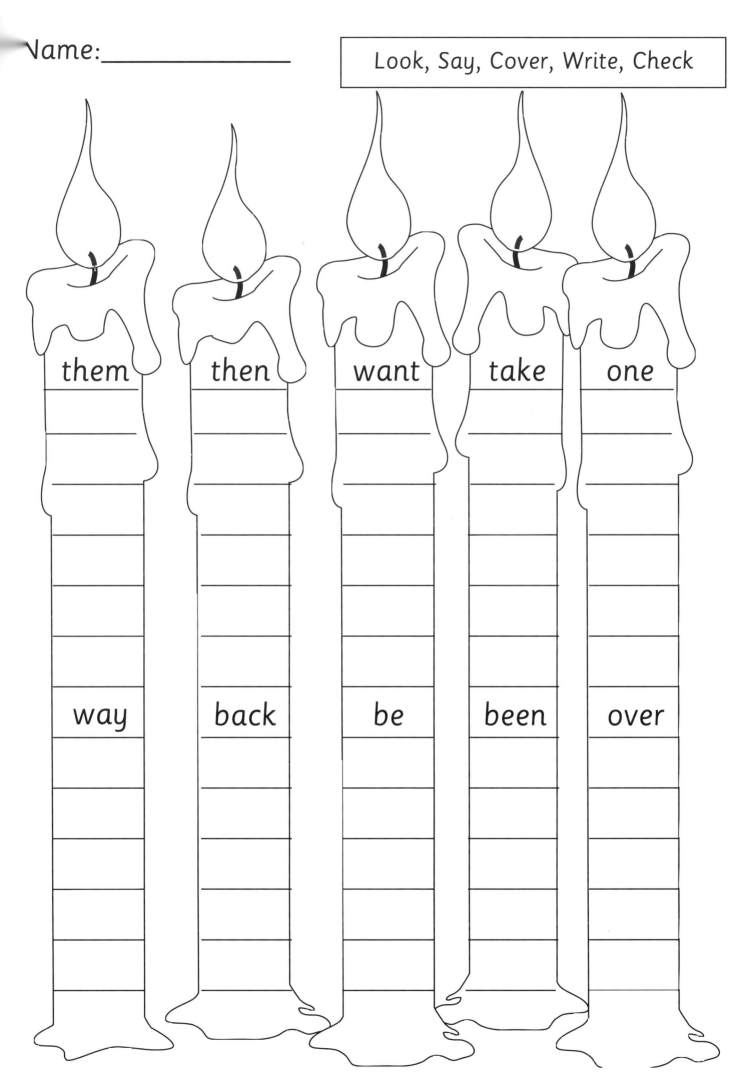

them

then

want

take

one

way

back

be

been

over

Name:_____

| bed | made | make |

Who is making the beds?

Put in the missing word. Write <u>make</u> or <u>made</u>

1. Alf _____ the beds yesterday.

2. Bet _____ the beds last week.

3. Mum will _____ the beds tomorrow.

Make a quilt with <u>be-</u> words

Who makes your bed?

bed    be__

Where do you put a quilt?

I _____

Make your own quilt.

Cut out the hexagon and make a quilt of <u>ma-</u> words on the back of this sheet.

Write the words here.

✏ made _____

✏ make _____

✏ bed _____

✏ made _____

ma__

Name:_____

| how | about |
|---|---|

Sort out these words into the pots -ow or -out.

**Alf**

**Bet**

| how | frown |
|---|---|
| now | shout |
| about | out |
| brown | down |
| snout | cow |
| trout | spout |

ow

_____
_____
_____
_____
_____

out

_____
_____
_____
_____
_____
_____

Colour how and about in different colours.

| how | about | now | about | now | how |
|---|---|---|---|---|---|
| out | now | how | cow | how | about |

 how  _____

 about  _____

Finish the sentence.

Alf:-  I want to go out for the day.

Bet:-  _____  _____ the fair?

Alf:-  I want something to eat.

Bet:-  _____ .

Ring all the **OW** words on this sheet.

Write about yourself on the back of this sheet.

**Alf**

Name:_____

Go over want and another in these sentences.

I _____ a mitten

Bet

I _____
_____ mitten

Change these words to want.

I changed

p a n t  ⟹  w a n t     | p | to | w |

w e n t  ⟹  __ __ __ __     |   | to |   |

w a r t  ⟹  __ __ __ __     |   | to |   |

w a n e  ⟹  __ __ __ __     |   | to |   |

Make words out of this word.     Can you make 10 words?

another

Fill in the missing words. Write want or another.

1. I _____ to do _____ sheet.

2. I _____ _____ sweet.

Sort out these sentences.

1.  want of cup I another tea.

✏️ _____

2.  want I in to run race. another

✏️ _____

© Topical Resources. May be photocopied for classroom use only.

Name:_____ | ball | by | be | back

Many words begin with <u>b</u>. My name begins with capital <u>B</u>

**Bet**

Fill in the missing letters.

<u>Across</u>

2. I kick a __ __ __ __.

3. I like to __ __ at school.

<u>Down</u>

1. Give it __ __ __ __.

3. It's __ __ the chair.

Fill in the missing words in the crossword. Follow the clues.

Find these words in the letter <u>b</u>. Colour them blue.

d b a l l c b e h n

d b a c k
c f b y a d

**Alf**

Ring all the words beginning with <u>b</u> in the play.

I'd like my ball back please, Bet.

It's over there by the fence. Would I be able to play with the ball later?

Yes, I'll bring the ball back.

Don't be too long. Where will you be?

I'll be in the field by the school.

How many?

ball ☐   by ☐   be ☐   back ☐

Name:_____

did       dig       door

Fill in the missing words
in the crossword.
Write did, dig or door.

**Alf**

Find these words in
the letter d. dig,
did, do.
Colour them red.

Follow the clues.

doordig
digdoor

didodid
didodid

Fill in the missing letters.

Sort out these
sentences.

## Across

1. I __ __ __ my homework.

4. I __ __ __ with my spade.

5. I open the __ __ __ __

## Down

1. Alf __ __ __ some housework.

2. Bet can __ __ __ with her spade.

3. Alf and Bet have a __ __ __ __ in

  their house

1.   the open I door.

   _____

2.   like dig. I to

   _____

3.   I work. did my.

   _____

We have a
d __ __ __
in our
house.

I like to
d__ __.

Name:_____

Where's Bet?

over here

Over here!

✏ over  _____ _____ _____

✏ here  _____ _____ _____

✏ over here  _____  _____

✏  _____  _____

Write and draw here.

Here is Bet's cake.

_____ is Alf's snake.

_____ is my _____.

_____.

Write **O** words jumping over the fence.

_____  _____

_____  _____  _____

Write over in the spaces.
Tick ✔ right ✘ wrong

Fill in the missing letters.

right   wrong

o __ e __        __ v __ r

1. I hide _____ the table.

2. This lesson is _____.

o v __ __        o __ __ __

__ __ __ r  __ __ e __

57

Name:_____

Fill in the <u>an</u> and then read the sentences.

1. Bet r_____ to the ice-cream van.

2. Alf ate _____ apple for lunch.

3. Bet found _____ ant under the bed.

4. Alf r_____ all the way home.

Draw and write.

an apple

an __gg

__ __ u__brell__

__ __ __nsec__

Remember! Use <u>an</u> if the next word begins with <u>a</u>, <u>e</u>, <u>i</u>, <u>o</u>, <u>u</u>.

a, e, i, o, u are vowels!

an
_____

Where did you run?

I ran _____

I ran _____

I ran _____

ran _____

_____

Underline every <u>an</u> word on this sheet

Name:_____

| must | will | not |
|---|---|---|

You <u>must</u> cross the road safely.

Fill in the missing words.

Ring the correct words.

You _____ stop, look and listen.

You _____ _____ run across the road.

Write <u>must</u> or <u>must not</u> under these pictures.

_____  _____  _____  _____

Write <u>will</u> or <u>will not</u> in these sentences.

Bet _____ talk to policemen.

Bet _____ talk to strangers.

Alf _____ eat an ice lolly.

Alf _____ eat an ice cream.

No thank you!

Colour <u>must</u> red. Colour <u>will</u> yellow.

| m | u | s | t | a | f | w | d | e | m |
|---|---|---|---|---|---|---|---|---|---|
| u | w | i | l | l | w | i | l | l | u |
| s | g | m | u | s | t | l | i | j | s |
| t | h | b | w | i | l | l | c | k | t |

must not
**mustn't**

will not
**won't**

Name:_____

us

them

Draw yourself and a friend.

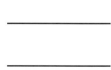
us

Bet    Alf

them

_____

_____

_____

_____

_____

_____

_____

_____

_____

Write us or them.

Who plays in your school yard? _____

Alf

Who tells you what to do on this sheet? _____

Tell us about your friends.

My friends are called _____ and _____.

Write us or them.

Bet

I play with _____ I like _____.

I would invite _____ to my party.

Tell us about your teachers.

The teachers tell _____ what to do.

They help _____ to do our work.

They give _____ a school report.

Put us in these words.

d _ _ t ⇨ _____      m _ _ h ⇨ _____

r _ _ t ⇨ _____      p _ _ h ⇨ _____

j _ _ t ⇨ _____      r _ _ h ⇨ _____

g _ _ t ⇨ _____      h _ _ h ⇨ _____

Name:_____

| if | then |
|---|---|

I wonder why......

Fill in the missing words. Write _if_ or _then_.

_____ a penguin has wings,

_____ why can't it fly?.

_____ a table has legs,

_____ why can't it walk?.

Colour _if_ red and _then_ yellow.

o f t h e n i f t h a n o f f i f t h e n

Do you know this song?

Fill in the missing word.

_____ you're happy and you know it - clap your hands.

_____ you're happy and you know it - nod your head.

_____ you're happy and you know it - stamp your feet.

Write the words.

✏ _if_ _____

✏ _then_ _____

t h e  +  [n]  ⟹  t h e n    _ _ _ _

t h e  +  [m]  ⟹  _ _ _ _    _ _ _ _

t h e  +  [y]  ⟹  _ _ _ _    _ _ _ _

t h e  +  [re]  ⟹  _ _ _ _ _    _ _ _ _ _

61

Name:_____

old | man

Do you know this song?

I know an old man called Michael Finnegan.

He grew whiskers on his chinnegan!

The wind came out and blew them in again.

Poor old Michael Finnegan!

Fill in the missing words.

I know an _____ _____ called Michael Finnegan.

He grew whiskers on _____ chinnegan!

Write the words here.

old _____

man _____

Here is another song about an old man.

1. This old man, he played one.

   He played nick-nack on my drum.

Can you write verse 2?

2. This _____ _____, he played _____.

   He played nick-nack on my shoe.

Ring the words <u>old</u> and <u>man</u> on this sheet.

Can you write more of this song on the back of this sheet.

Name:_____

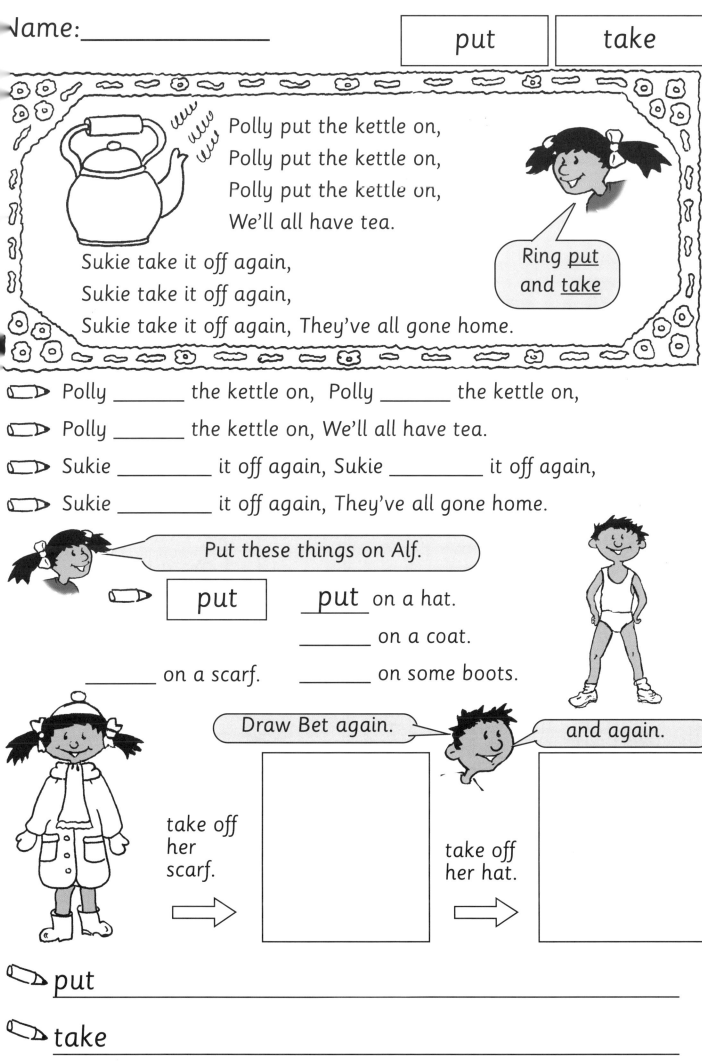

put

take

Polly put the kettle on,
Polly put the kettle on,
Polly put the kettle on,
We'll all have tea.

Sukie take it off again,
Sukie take it off again,
Sukie take it off again, They've all gone home.

Ring put and take

Polly _____ the kettle on,  Polly _____ the kettle on,

Polly _____ the kettle on, We'll all have tea.

Sukie _____ it off again, Sukie _____ it off again,

Sukie _____ it off again, They've all gone home.

Put these things on Alf.

put    _put_ on a hat.

_____ on a coat.

_____ on a scarf.    _____ on some boots.

Draw Bet again.    and again.

take off her scarf.

take off her hat.

put _____

take _____

Name:_____

| had | girl | bed | house |
|------|-------|------|-------|
| saw | three | came | down |

Can you read this story?

Goldilocks and the three bears

Once upon a time there was a little girl called Goldilocks.

One day she saw a house in the woods which belonged to the three bears.

She went inside and saw some porridge.

She had some!

She saw a chair. She sat on it and broke it!

She went upstairs and saw a bed. She had a lie down and fell asleep.

The three bears came home

Find these words and colour them. How many times did you find them?

had ☐    house ☐    came ☐

girl ☐    saw ☐    down ☐

bed ☐    three ☐

Finish this story on the back of this sheet.